House of Commons
Welsh Affairs Committee

Cross-border health arrangements between England and Wales

Third Report of Session 2014–15

Report, together with formal minutes relating to the report

*Ordered by the House of Commons
to be printed 10 March 2015*

HC 404
Published on 12 March 2015
by authority of the House of Commons
London: The Stationery Office Limited
£11.00

The Welsh Affairs Committee

The Welsh Affairs Committee is appointed by the House of Commons to examine the expenditure, administration, and policy of the Office of the Secretary of State for Wales (including relations with the National Assembly for Wales).

Current membership

David T.C. Davies MP *(Conservative, Monmouth) (Chair)*
Guto Bebb MP *(Conservative, Aberconwy)*
Geraint Davies MP *(Labour, Swansea West)*
Glyn Davies MP *(Conservative, Montgomeryshire)*
Stephen Doughty MP *(Labour, Cardiff South and Penarth)*
Jonathan Edwards MP *(Plaid Cymru, Carmarthen East and Dinefwr)*
Nia Griffith MP *(Labour, Llanelli)*
Simon Hart MP *(Conservative, Carmarthen West and South Pembrokeshire)*
Mrs Siân C. James MP *(Labour, Swansea East)*
Karen Lumley MP *(Conservative, Redditch)*
Jessica Morden MP *(Labour, Newport East)*
Mr Mark Williams MP *(Liberal Democrat, Ceredigion)*

The following Members were also members of the Committee during this Parliament

Stuart Andrew MP *(Conservative, Pudsey)*
Alun Cairns MP *(Conservative, Vale of Glamorgan)*
Susan Elan Jones MP *(Labour, Clwyd South)*
Owen Smith MP *(Labour, Pontypridd)*
Robin Walker MP *(Conservative, Worcester)*
Hywel Williams MP *(Plaid Cymru, Arfon)*

Powers

The Committee is one of the departmental select committees, the powers of which are set out in House of Commons Standing Orders, principally in SO No 152. These are available on the internet via http://www.parliament.uk/

Publications

The Reports and evidence of the Committee are published by The Stationery Office by Order of the House. All publications of the Committee (including press notices) are on the internet at Welsh Affairs Committee - UK Parliament

The Reports of the Committee, the formal minutes relating to that report, oral evidence taken and some or all written evidence are available in printed volumes.

Additional written evidence may be published on the internet only.

Committee staff

The current staff of the Committee is Richard Ward (Clerk), Anwen Rees (Committee Specialist), Shane Murray (Senior Committee Assistant), Baris Tufekci (Committee Assistant), and Jessica Bridges-Palmer (Media Officer).

Contacts

All correspondence should be addressed to the Clerk of the Welsh Affairs Committee, House of Commons, 14 Tothill Street, London SW1H 9NB. The telephone number for general enquiries is 020 7219 3264; and the Committee's email address is welshcom@parliament.uk

Contents

Summary

The border between Wales and England is approximately 170 miles long, with 50% of the population of Wales living within 25 miles of the border. As a result cross-border movements are a fact of life, including for healthcare. Since devolution, there has been increasing divergence between the healthcare systems of England and Wales. This can cause confusion for patients, particularly those who rely on healthcare facilities on either side of the border from where they live.

During our inquiry, we sought to bring clarity to a number of issues and to examine what services cross-border patients are entitled to receive. We also examined the different funding and commissioning arrangements in England and Wales, and hope that our report sheds light on the arrangements for the funding of cross-border healthcare.

Our inquiry has not been concerned with the merits of the healthcare system in Wales, which is devolved to the Welsh Government, or England. Instead, our report focused on areas where there was need for essential and detailed systems of liaison to be in place to guarantee consistent cross-border co-ordination.

The Committee's key recommendations and conclusions are:

- We welcome the commitment from the Welsh Government's Health Minister on patient needs and his commitment not to allow the border to become a barrier. We recognise that Welsh GPs will be mindful of a need to maintain investment and capacity in Wales. Healthcare providers in England and Wales need to maintain close links to ensure that patients receive the treatment they need regardless of their country of residence, particularly given the policy divergence that has emerged as a result of devolution.

- We recommend that the UK Government and the Welsh Government work together to examine how improvements can be made in the electronic transfer of information between Wales and England.

- We recommend that the Department of Health works with its counterparts in the devolved administrations to establish a single Performers List for GPs across the UK.

- We recommend that the Department of Health and the Welsh Government work together with medical practitioners, particularly at a GP level, to ensure that patients are better informed of the differences in healthcare policy between England and Wales. Patients must also be made aware of the impact of choosing a Welsh or English GP and the implications that this might have for later care.

- We recommend that NHS Wales and NHS England work together to improve patient engagement for cross-border services.

- We are concerned that there is a lack of communication regarding changes to healthcare services which could have an impact across the border. We recommend that formal protocols are put in place to ensure consultation between LHBs and CCGs when changes to services impact on populations across the border.

In this report, **conclusions are printed in bold** and ***recommendations are printed in bold italics.***

1   Introduction

1. The border between Wales and England is approximately 170 miles long, with 50% of the population of Wales living within 25 miles of the border. As a result, cross-border movements are a fact of life, including for healthcare. Since devolution, there has been increasing divergence between the healthcare systems of England and Wales. These differences in policy and administration have implications for patients who rely on healthcare facilities on the other side of the border from where they live.

2. In April 2013, NHS Wales and NHS England agreed a revised Protocol for Cross-border Healthcare Services to improve the interaction between the NHS on either side of the England-Wales border.

3. We chose to examine cross-border healthcare because we had heard of significant confusion amongst patients needing to travel across the border for treatment, for example, in knowing what they were entitled to receive from their health service. Our inquiry has not been concerned with the merits of the healthcare system in Wales, which is devolved to the Welsh Government and scrutinised by the National Assembly for Wales, or England. Given the likelihood of further health policy divergence in the future, we believe that it is essential for robust and detailed systems of liaison to be in place to guarantee consistent cross-border co-ordination in years to come.

4. We took oral evidence from patient representatives, professional bodies in the healthcare profession, Welsh Local Health Boards, English Clinical Commissioning Groups, along with the Welsh and UK Governments. A full list of witnesses can be found at the end of this Report.

5. We also took the opportunity during this inquiry to engage with a wider section of the population. We held a web forum to allow people to submit their personal experiences of cross-border healthcare, from which we received 36 written submissions. We also held public events in conjunction with Parliamentary Outreach in Newtown and Hereford to hear from members of the public, medical practitioners and local representatives. These were well attended and greatly informed our inquiry. A summary of the events is attached as an Annex. We wish to place on record our gratitude to all those who have contributed to our inquiry, especially those who attended the events in Newtown and Hereford.

2   Cross-border health services

6. Healthcare pathways for patients have always crossed the Welsh-English border. Healthcare is divided into primary, secondary, and tertiary services and cross-border issues are present in all three categories to some degree.

Primary Care

7. Primary healthcare covers the activities of a healthcare provider who acts as a first point of consultation for all patients, such as GP services, dentistry services, ophthalmic services and pharmacy services. Approximately 20,800 English patients are registered with Welsh or Welsh-registered GPs.[1] Approximately 15,000 Welsh residents are registered with English or English-registered GPs.[2] There is therefore a net flow of approximately 6,000 patients into Welsh primary care from England.[3] We were told that convenience is the main reason behind cross-border travel for primary healthcare. Patients receiving treatment for primary care services on the other side of the border generally live in immediate border areas along the Wales-England border and choose a GP surgery as close to home as possible, which may not be in their country of residence.[4]

Secondary Care

8. Secondary healthcare are services which are generally provided in or by general hospitals. Although the flow is generally from Wales to England, the cross-border flow does differ from north to south Wales. For example, the cross-border flow in Betsi Cadwaladr University Health Board and Powys Teaching Health Board predominately relates to residents in Wales going into England. This is partly for reasons of convenience, but also because of the lack of secondary care in some areas (Powys, for example, has no District General Hospital).[5] Meanwhile, in Aneurin Bevan University Health Board, the cross-border flow predominately relates to English residents who are registered with Welsh GPs.[6] In 2012-13, approximately 50,700 Welsh residents travelled to non-Welsh providers for treatment, including both emergency and elective patients.[7] In the same year, 10,370 non-Welsh patients were admitted to Welsh hospitals.[8]

---

1   Welsh-registered GPs refers to GP surgeries located in England which have contracts with NHS Wales.

2   English-registered GPs refers to GP surgeries located in Wales which have contracts with NHS England. There is one practice in contract with NHS England that has a surgery in Wales: the Meadows Medical Practice has a surgery at Knighton (in Powys LHB).

3   Welsh Government (CBH0051)

4   Q14, Q83, Q94

5   Q6

6   Welsh NHS Confederation (CBH0016)

7   NHS Wales Annual PEDW data: 2012/13 Provider based headline figures

8   NHS Wales Annual PEDW data: 2012/13 Resident based headline figures

Tertiary Care

9. Tertiary services are provided by specialist hospitals or regional centres equipped with diagnostic and treatment facilities not generally available at local hospitals. Referral is generally from a secondary care specialist. Examples include advanced neonatology, genetic services, plastic surgery and burns treatment centres, and organ transplantation. Tertiary care centres are located in areas of higher population and the relatively small population size of North and Mid-Wales means there is not the critical mass of people needed to support more local specialised services.[9] Cross-border flows for patients for such services are therefore mostly from Wales into England.[10]

Devolution and policy divergence

10. Since devolution, the NHS in Wales has been a responsibility of the Welsh Government. Since 1999, the identification and pursuit of different health policy priorities by the four nations of the UK has led to the adoption of different models for the provision and organisation of health services. The healthcare policies of England and Wales have diverged in some areas. Some of the ways in which healthcare policies of England and Wales have diverged are set out below.

Internal Market

11. A major policy divergence relates to the differences in the way services are commissioned and funded. England has a national tariff system called Payments by Results (PbR) where each individual treatment is billed to the NHS at a standard rate. Payment by Results is intended to encourage Clinical Commissioning Groups to commission only those services they need, and to establish an incentive for providers to attract more patients and complete a higher number of procedures at a lower unit cost. Welsh Local Health Boards do not operate a tariff system and largely rely on block contracts based on historical data.

Foundation Trusts

12. In England, hospitals have the ability to apply for foundation trust status. Foundation trusts are run by a board drawn from local organisations and communities. The declared intention behind this policy is to make hospitals more responsive to the needs and wishes of their local community.[11] Foundation trusts do not exist in Wales.

'Patient voice' and 'Patient choice'

13. England has implemented 'patient choice' in booking elective treatments. Patients have the right to choose which hospital they are referred to by their GP. In contrast, in Wales,

---

9   Q297, Q303

10   Q301

11   www.policy-network.net/uploadedFiles/Publications/Publications/Millburn.pdf

unlike in England, there are community health councils whose remit is to ensure patients' views and needs influence policies and plans. The Welsh Government has also stated that it will give patients a greater say in their services, with a focus on 'patient voice'.

Waiting time targets

14. Waiting time targets in England and Wales differ. The maximum waiting time in England is 18 weeks from the time of referral to a hospital consultant to the beginning of treatment. Local Health Boards in Wales work to a maximum waiting time target of 26 weeks from referral to start of treatment.[12]

Cancer Drugs Fund

15. The UK Government's Cancer Drugs Fund, worth £280 million in 2014-15 and an estimated £340 million in 2015–2016, came into effect on 1 April 2011.[13] The fund is for cancer drugs that are not routinely available on the NHS. This may include drugs that have not been approved for funding, are yet to be approved, or that are not approved for a specific type of cancer. In May 2012, the Welsh Government rejected the need for a Cancer Drugs Fund in Wales due to the different processes in Wales. In Wales, the NHS relies on National Institute for Health and Care Excellence (NICE) guidance and the All Wales Medicines Strategy Group (AWMSG) for its expert advice on medications. The Welsh Health Specialised Services Committee told us that this was meant to ensure that no preference was given between cancer patients and others.[14]

Free Prescriptions

16. Since 2007, NHS patients in Wales have received free prescriptions, including all patients registered with a Welsh GP who collect their prescriptions from Welsh pharmacists and those patients with an English GP as long as they collect the prescription from a Welsh pharmacist and present their entitlement card. In its written evidence, the Department of Health noted that approximately 90% of prescriptions in England are provided free of charge, due to various entitlements, so the financial impact on the public purse of the difference between the two systems in respect of this policy is not as great as it first might seem.[15]

---

12 The targets apply to the majority of referrals to NHS hospitals for treatment; however, there are a number of exceptions. In addition, some conditions such as cancer have their own specific target.

13 www.england.nhs.uk/2015/01/12/cancer-drug-budget/

14 Q308

15 Department of Health (CBH0055)

3   Funding and Commissioning

17. Health services in England and Wales are subject to different funding and commissioning arrangements, which can result in confusion and misunderstanding by patients, and indeed sometimes by staff. We have sought to shed light on the arrangements for funding of cross-border healthcare.

Commissioning arrangements

18. In England, 211 Clinical Commissioning Groups (CCGs), overseen by NHS England, are legally responsible for the commissioning of health services. CCGs are clinician-led groups that include all of the GP groups in their geographical area. The aim of this is to give GPs and other clinicians the power to influence commissioning decisions for their patients.[16] Clinical commissioning groups work with patients and healthcare professionals and in partnership with local communities and local authorities. CCGs operate by commissioning healthcare services including: elective hospital care; rehabilitation care; urgent and emergency care; most community health services; and mental health and learning disability services.

19. In Wales, seven Local Health Boards (LHBs) are responsible for planning and delivering medical services, and aim to integrate specialist, secondary, community and primary care and health improvements. In general, this means that LHBs are largely responsible for commissioning all primary and secondary care. Tertiary and highly specialised services are commissioned in Wales through a joint committee: the Welsh Health Specialised Services Committee (WHSSC). A diagram showing the structure of NHS England and NHS Wales is below.

---

16   Health and Social Care Act 2012, Part 1 and Schedule 2

Structure of the NHS in England

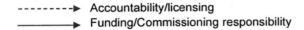

- - - - - - - ▶ Accountability/licensing
————————▶ Funding/Commissioning responsibility

Post April 2013 structure

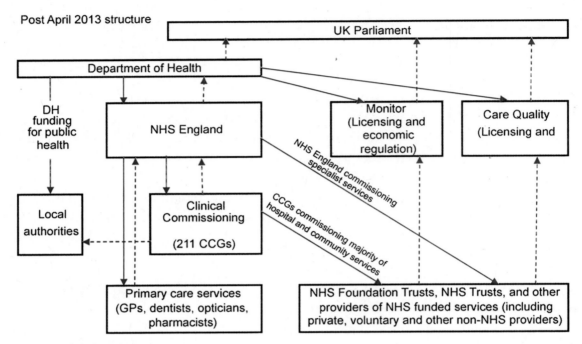

Source: House of Commons Library

Structure of NHS in Wales

- - - - - - - ▶ Accountability/licensing
————————▶ Funding/Commissioning responsibility

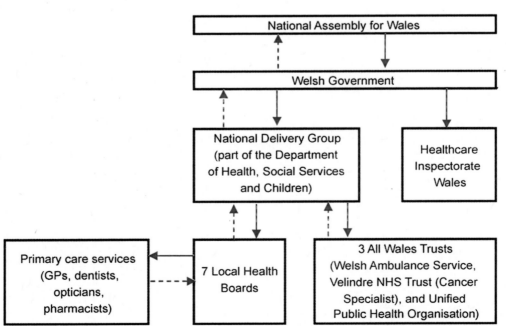

Source: Wales Audit Office

Cross-border Protocol

20. The Protocol for Cross-border Healthcare Services[17] sets out which body is responsible for commissioning care for people who live on one side of the border, but are registered with a GP on the other.[18] The protocol provides that the operational responsibility for commissioning services for a patient is determined by GP registration, rather than residency. Under the protocol, Welsh residents who are registered with an English GP or English-registered GP are 'English' patients. Likewise English residents who are registered with a Welsh GP or a Welsh-registered GP are considered 'Welsh' patients.

21. Paragraph 11 of the protocol summarises the commissioning and healthcare planning responsibilities and legally responsible bodies.

Residency	GP Location	Commissioning/healthcare planning responsibility	Legally Responsible Body
Wales	Wales	LHB	LHB
England	England	CCG	CCG
Wales	England	CCG	LHB
England	Wales	LHB	CCG

22. Paragraph 16 of the protocol summarises what patients should be able to expect in terms of standards for access to health care dependency on residency, GP location and provider:

Residency	GP Location	English Provider to meet:	Welsh Provider to meet:
Wales	Wales	WG standards	WG standards
England	Wales	WG standards	WG standards
England	England	NHS Constitution	WG standards
Wales	England	NHS Constitution	WG standards

Compatibility of the Cross-border Protocol and NHS Constitution

23. In England, the Health and Social Care Act 2012 and the NHS Constitution gives certain rights to English residents, including the right to choose their hospital, and sets maximum waiting times targets.[19] However, as we have set out earlier in this Chapter, English residents who have a Welsh GP or a Welsh-registered GP are considered 'Welsh' patients and therefore treated to Welsh Government standards.

---

17   Protocol for Cross-border Healthcare Services, April 2013

18   The protocol has been annually or biannually since 2005. The current protocol runs from April 2013 until 2016.

19   The National Health Service Commissioning Board and Clinical Commissioning Groups (Responsibilities and Standing Rules) Regulations 2012

24. Witnesses told us that English law and the cross-border protocol were incompatible, and had led to English residents being denied their legal rights. Action4OurCare[20] said that:

> The Health and Social Care Act is really clear. It applies to absolutely everybody who lives in England. The cross-border protocol has overwritten that, but it has no authority or mandate to do so. The legislation should stand for the English and for the Welsh Government. You should make sure that, whatever you do with devolution, you do not deny English residents their rights.[21]

25. Witnesses told us that this particularly affected residents in Hereford and Gloucestershire. Jesse Norman MP explained that over 3,500 patients in Hereford had no choice but to register with a Welsh surgery as they lived in a location not served by an English practice.[22] In Gloucestershire, approximately 10,000 patients are affected, while residents in Gloucestershire also face the situation that a number of GP surgeries, while physically based in England, are registered in Wales.[23] At our public sessions, some attendees resident in England told us that when they had requested a transfer to a GP's surgery in England, they had been turned away.

26. In oral evidence, Mr Norman called for English rights under the NHS Constitution to be recognised under the protocol:

> I am just insisting on the very obvious [...] point that if people live in England and have no choice but to use a Welsh GP, they should maintain their rights under the English NHS. They are owed that duty of care. There is a parallel case for Welsh patients who are in the other situation.[24]

27. Shropshire Clinical Commissioning Group commented that currently Welsh providers did not offer a dual service for the English-responsible patient and treated them with the Welsh targets "even though we would pay for it".[25] It told us that: "it is only a matter of time before an English resident who is registered with a Welsh GP challenges that".[26]

28. In response, Jane Ellison MP, Parliamentary Under-Secretary of State for Public Health, told us that she had established that there was an inconsistency between the protocol and the legislative position. She had written to Mark Drakeford AM, Minister for

---

20   Action4OurCare is a non-party political, not for profit action group which was set up in March 2013 by a number of Gloucestershire residents.

21   Q64

22   Jesse Norman MP (CHB0018)

23   There are four practices in contract with the Welsh NHS that have surgeries in England. In the area of Shropshire CCG, the Chirk practice has a surgery in Oswestry. In the area of Gloucestershire CCG (more specifically, in the Forest of Dean) there are 3 practices: the Wye Valley Practice has a surgery at St Briavels; the Vauxhall Practice has a surgery at Tutshill; and the Towngate Practice has a surgery at Sedbury.

24   Q48

25   Q125

26   Q127

Health and Social Services in the Welsh Government, to raise the issue with him. She told us that there were three scenarios:

> As part of the work that we are taking forward with the Welsh Government, we want to resolve the problem around the rights of English residents. I can see three theoretical scenarios here. The first is that one attempts to close the border and accepts that the two systems are totally separate. It seems to me that that runs contrary to the whole spirit of the conversation that we have been having here this morning and to putting the interest of patients and communities paramount, so I do not think that is the right solution.

> The second approach is simply to recognise that English patients who are registered with Welsh practices do not receive their NHS constitution rights in relation to either a legal entitlement to choice or maximum waiting times. Clearly, that is very problematic and is not something that we can duck. We need to find a way of addressing that.

> The third option is that those patients who are registered with Welsh practices receive English standards and entitlements. That contrasts with policies of the Welsh Government as to the equal treatment of Welsh-resident and English-resident patients on a GP's list. We are working with the Welsh Government to try to resolve that conundrum.[27]

29. During our evidence session with Mr Drakeford, we asked whether the Welsh Government was prepared to recognise the rights that English residents are afforded under the Health and Social Care Act 2012. He told us that

> The system we have [...] is that if you sign up with a Welsh GP you get the package that goes with that, and if you sign up with an English GP you get the package that goes with that. I understand that in England the Department of Health believes that this causes some difficulties to them in terms of English law. It causes no difficulties to us in Wales; but we are having discussions. [...] I am happy to be as helpful as I can, but the problem is not mine, and the solution is not mine ...[28]

30. **There is an unresolved tension between the cross-border healthcare protocol and the Health and Social Care Act 2012. English patients registered with Welsh GPs or Welsh-registered GPs do not receive the same services as if they were registered with an English GP, and for the majority of people concerned, they will not have a choice of registering with an English GP.**

31. *The Department of Health should investigate the problem of why some patients living in England, currently being treated in the Welsh healthcare system and wishing to be treated in the English healthcare system, have been turned away by GP practices in*

England. This should be considered in light of the legal rights of these residents under the Health and Social Care Act 2012.

32. *We recommend that the Welsh and UK Governments continue to work together to clarify what an English patient registered with a Welsh GP and a Welsh-registered GP, and a Welsh patient registered with an English GP and an English-registered GP, can expect.*

Funding

Primary services

33. In the case of primary services provided across the border, which include GP services, dentistry, and ophthalmic services, there is no funding flow between England and Wales. The Department of Health told us that:

> … no transfers have ever been made between the English NHS and the NHSs in other parts of the UK to reflect the use residents of one part of the UK make of primary care services provided in another part of the UK.[29]

Any costs lie where they fall. This was described to us as a 'knock for knock' arrangement based on historical funding flows.

34. Mr Drakeford told us that this was a sensible way to do things. He explained:

> The alternative is to bill one another for all the different treatments that go on. My view is that that would create a big industry of accountants following bits of activity and we would end up paying more to create the system than we would save in other ways. On the whole, the system is satisfactory to both sides as it is. We pick up costs in Wales for some people who live in England, and the English system picks up some costs in England for people who live in Wales. Those costs are not sufficiently significant to erect an industry around them to pursue them in an accountancy way. The system broadly balances itself out.[30]

Secondary and Tertiary services

35. In the case of secondary care services provided to patients with a GP 'across the border', a net funding transfer is agreed annually between the Department of Health and the Welsh Government, in recognition of the additional secondary care costs that fall on the Welsh NHS. This is set out in the cross-border protocol, which confirms that there will be no financial shortfall on the part of any LHB or CCG in providing secondary healthcare services to the other country's residents.

---

29   Department of Health (CBH0049)

30   Q348

36. The Welsh Government currently receives £5.8 million per annum from the Department of Health. This is based on 2008-09 calculations, when it was calculated that 20,000 English residents were registered with Welsh GPs or Welsh-registered GPs compared to 15,000 Welsh residents registered with English GPs, giving a net import of 5,000 English residents. This figure is then multiplied by the Hospital and Community Health Service (HCHS) spend per resident of £1,145.[31]

37. In oral evidence, the Welsh Government's Health Minister said that our investigations had helped "expose the fact" that the formula had not been updated since 2008. He suggested that the transfer amount "had we increased the funding by 5% every year, because that is how much the costs have increased", should now be £9.1 million.[32]

38. We were told that the Welsh Government distributed these transferred funds to the LHBs that had treated those patients from across the border: "people who live in England might receive primary care at Aneurin Bevan, but if they are treated at a hospital in Cardiff, the funding will go to Cardiff. The funding goes where the treatment is given".[33]

39. In the case of secondary and tertiary services commissioned in England for patients resident in Wales with a GP in Wales, Welsh LHBs and WHSSC make payments for activity undertaken by English NHS providers, either under contractual or non-contractual arrangements. This activity is charged by English providers at English tariff (Payment by Results) rates.[34] It is less common for English residents registered with GPs in England to seek treatment in Wales, but where this does occur, Welsh LHBs and NHS Trust providers charge English CCGs for the activity based on their local calculated cost.

40. During our public events, we heard concerns among Welsh patients that they could be refused treatment in English hospitals because of a shortfall of money from Welsh LHBs. Many of these statements were based on high-profile events that largely took place in a particular time frame.[35] Betsi Cadwaladr University Health Board reassured us that financial planning had improved, and that Welsh LHBs were developing three-year plans to allow more integrated planning, which would take into account population demands and known flows.[36] We also heard that some English-based providers had failed to invoice Welsh Local Health Boards within the agreed timeframe.

41. Shropshire Clinical Commissioning Group told us that relationships between LHB and CCGs had improved and there was a "lot more dialogue at all levels: in front-line services, among senior management and at executive—even Chief Executive—level".[37] The

---

31   Welsh Government (CBH0051)

32   Q344

33   Q343

34   The Department of Health publishes national tariffs every year.

35   For example: in 2008, the North Bristol NHS Trust refused to admit patients from Wales after the Welsh NHS refused to pay the going rate for treatment; in 2011, the Liverpool Heart and Chest Hospital banned patients from North Wales from having elective surgery after Betsi Cadwaladr University Health Board failed to provide funding for their treatment.

36   Q26

37   Q110

Department of Health informed us that greater transparency would be available from 2014-15 onwards, as the Department would hold central information on monies owed by Welsh LHBs.[38]

42. We welcome the good relationship between Local Health Boards in Wales and the Clinical Commissioning Groups in England. The publication of the financial accounts of such bodies will enable the public to see whether value for money is being achieved.

4   Cross-border problems

43. During our inquiry, witnesses identified three issues in particular that have significant impact on cross-border healthcare: access to services; the lack of IT compatibility between England and Wales; and the difficulties surrounding GP Performers Lists. We examine all of these areas in more detail in turn.

Access to Services

44. Many of the people we met in Newtown and Hereford expressed concern about difficulties and delays accessing secondary and specialist services on a cross-border basis. They were particularly concerned by a perceived move towards 'in country' commissioning on the part of the Welsh Government with the ultimate aim of treating all Welsh patients within the country, and felt that on some occasions this was not in the patient's interest. This issue also dominated the comments we received on the webforum. Box 1 below includes some of the submissions we received on this issue.

Comment 1

… at the end of 2013 we were told that the Aneurin Bevan University Health Board was no longer willing to fund her treatment in Hereford and she would have to return to the Wales NHS as they wished to keep expenditure within Wales […] I believe they chose not to treat to save on expenses. We are treated as 2nd class citizens of the UK compared to England.

Comment 2

My wife, who was undergoing ongoing treatment for a life threatening condition in Bristol, had her cross border funding withdrawn by the Aneurin Bevan University Health Board. Her consultant himself telephoned to say that he could not see her the following week as was planned. To see a 'new' consultant in Wales would have meant a delay of many weeks.

Comment 3

It is not at all easy for a Welsh resident to access NHS care in England. My GP is registered with Wales NHS but the surgery I attend is in England. I have had to fight to see a specialist in England because of long waiting times in Wales. My GP applied for "out of area funding" from Wales in November 2013. This was refused. An appeal in December 2013 was refused the following January. […] It's monstrous for patients on the border because we cannot access the right people all in the same area. We are a UNITED Kingdom but not when it comes to Health. I feel that Wales NHS has been deliberately obstructive.

---

45. We found that many of the concerns related to a policy introduced by Aneurin Bevan University Health Board (ABUHB) in September 2012. At this time, ABUHB had

introduced a policy aimed at minimising referrals out of the LHB's area or outside Wales. It described the aim of the policy as being that:

> … the Health Board is the primary provider of secondary care services for the registered/resident population of Gwent […]

> Where this cannot be provided by the Health Board's own services for reasons such as resources, expertise or capacity, then the Health Board will look to plan and secure the necessary services with other NHS Providers in Wales through its agreed care pathways. Where the services cannot be provided by the Health Board or with other Welsh providers, the Health Board will plan and secure services from other appropriate providers.[39]

46. This policy caused concern to patients and medical practitioners. The policy affected Welsh residents seeking to have treatment in England and English residents with Welsh-registered GPs—even when, for a small number of patients, that GP surgery was physically situated in England.

47. ABUHB explained that the policy was introduced immediately following the establishment of LHBs. It had been introduced in recognition that there were Welsh residents going out of area for services that could be more centralised. It acknowledged that the policy had particularly affected English residents with Welsh-registered GPs who had "normal and historic[al] flows" to English hospitals:

> The error that we made was, I think for our English residents on the border registered with Welsh GPs, when we asked them to seek prior approval. We had a lot of appeals as part of that process.[40]

48. Following its own review, ABUHB changed its policy and agreed that from 1 September 2013 English residents with a Welsh GP did not require prior approval to be referred for routine secondary care to a small number of English providers.[41]

49. While we welcome this decision, which has made it easier for English residents to access secondary care closer to their home, there is currently no change for Welsh residents. For a referral to any English providers as a Welsh resident prior approval continues to be required. We therefore sought assurances that there was not a deliberate policy in place to stop cross-border health movement of Welsh patients wishing to access services in England.

50. Mr Drakeford told us that the Welsh Government was focused on providing the best care to all those needed it, whether that was in Wales or across the border in England:

---

39   Taken from page 6 of the Policy for Out of Area Referrals for Secondary Care, issued by the Aneurin Bevan University Health Board, May 2012.

40   Q30

41   Hereford Hospital (Wye Valley NHS Trust), Frenchay & Southmead Hospitals (North Bristol NHS Trust), United Bristol NHS Trust Hospitals and Lydney & the Dilke Hospitals (Gloucestershire Care Services)

Our aim is to make sure that people get the treatment they need in the best place for them. Sometimes, that will mean that we are able to move treatments closer to people's homes and to bring services back across the border. But sometimes, services across the border will still be the best for Welsh patients. So I do not have a principle that says, 'Treatments for Welsh patients should be provided in Wales.' That is not my starting point.[42]

51. **Cross-border movements have been a fact of life for many years, and this is no less the case for health services. For those residing in immediate border areas, the nearest health provider may not be in their country of residence. There is no practical or realistic prospect of diverting these well-established cross-border flows, nor would it be desirable to do so.**

52. **We welcome the commitment from the Welsh Government's Health Minister on patient needs and his commitment not to allow the border to become a barrier. We recognise that Welsh GPs will be mindful of a need to maintain investment and capacity in Wales. Healthcare providers in England and Wales need to maintain close links to ensure that patients receive the treatment they need regardless of their country of residence, particularly given the policy divergence that has emerged as a result of devolution.**

Tertiary Services

53. The way in which Welsh health providers commissions specialised healthcare from English providers was also raised as an issue. Specialised services are commissioned on a national basis by the Welsh Health Specialised Services Committee (WHSSC), a joint committee of the seven Local Health boards in Wales. The majority of specialised care commissioned from English providers (between 95% and 99%) is done through service level agreements, where contracts are already in place to treat Welsh patients. This is provided directly on the basis of a direct clinical referral, usually from a secondary/tertiary care clinician in Wales, to one of the designated centres in England. In total, WHSSC currently manages 34 healthcare contracts with NHS England providers to the value of £100 million.[43]

54. WHSSC told us that these contracts represented a "very positive set of relationships" between Wales and England.[44] However, it expressed concern that it was not always possible to formalise service level agreements (SLAs) and sign contracts due to key differences in the contract documents. It cited issues such as the fact Wales did not operate the patient choice scheme, differences in access criteria and waiting time targets. WHSSC told us that a review was needed of SLAs.[45]

---

42   Q357

43   Welsh Health Specialised Services Committee (CBH0040)

44   Q297

45   Q321

55. There are some conditions and treatments which fall outside of the contracts that WHSCC already has in place with specialist centres in England, either because they are excluded from the payment by results mechanism or they are not normally commissioned. In these circumstances clinicians apply on the behalf of patients either for prior approval (for a limited number of conditions due to their rarity or high cost treatment) or through Individual Patient Funding Requests (for service not normally commissioned) where patients must apply through the "exceptionality" criteria. WHSSC told us that they managed Individual Patient Funding requests (IPFR) and non-contracted activity to the value of £6 million per annum.[46]

56. Witnesses expressed concerns about these two processes, and told us there was a lack of knowledge amongst clinicians of the referral processes. Genetic Alliance UK told the Committee that both systems required the same application form to be used, which led to "great confusion for the responsible clinician".[47] The Royal College of Physicians said that the forms were "laborious and an administrative waste of time".[48]

57. We also heard concerns about the length of time it took to get approval for a referral to a specialist in England. Genetic Alliance UK told us that some patients had waited "a few years" to have their application processed, and such delays led to "negative consequences" for patients with a delay in diagnosis and inability to access targeted treatments.[49]

58. When we questioned WHSCC about delays in the process, they told us that they aimed to be "very timely" in their approval process. They told us that there was a two-day turnaround for prior approvals, while there were monthly panels for requests done via IPFR process, with "virtual panels" organised for urgent situations. They cited a recent example where they had held a virtual panel to expedite cancer treatment involving HIPEC heated chemotherapy.[50]

59. However, they told us that a lack of knowledge about the process and the forms amongst clinicians in Wales did cause delays. For example, many of the delays that occurred were as a result of not receiving the correct clinical information from referring clinicians. This would involve the panel going back to the clinician for further information: "if we have challenged back [...] we need two or three weeks to get the right diagnostics done, to get the right preparation of the case brought forward, so when we do make a decision it is the right decision for the patient".[51]

60. Witnesses agreed that there was a need for further education regarding the process of patient referral for specialised services.[52]

---

46   Welsh Health Specialised Services Committee (CBH0040)

47   Genetic Alliance UK (CHB0020)

48   Q180

49   Genetic Alliance UK (CHB0020)

50   Q309

51   Q310

52   Q315

61. **Specialised services are accessed by patients from all across Wales. It is unacceptable that administrative issues lead to delays to patients seeking specialised services.** *We recommend that Welsh Local Health Boards must provide improved training for clinicians on how to refer patients for tertiary care.*

62. **The divergence in policy since devolution can cause difficulties in cross-border contracts. There must be improvements to service level agreements (SLAs) between LHBs and CCGs.** *We recommend that the Department of Health and the Welsh Government work together to carry out a review of cross-border SLAs.*

63. **Uncertainty in the referral process can cause unnecessary worry to patients and their families, particularly when they are their most vulnerable. Decisions must be made in a timely manner.** *We recommend that a 30-day limit be placed on decisions on referrals by WHSSC.*

Information technology compatibility

64. There are different IT systems in use in the healthcare systems in Wales and in England, and indeed, systems vary even within the English system. During our inquiry, we heard that this made it difficult for primary and secondary/tertiary systems in England and Wales to communicate with each other.

65. Healthcare professionals told us that the current lack of compatibility of IT systems was affecting patient care, causing delay to results and potentially putting patients at risk. Dr Frank Joseph from the Royal College of Physicians described how his inability to access blood tests taken in Wales had an impact on patient care when diabetes sufferers visited him at the Countess of Chester Hospital in England:

> When patients are referred to me I see them. We try to do a shared case management strategy. I see them maybe every six months or a year, and in the interim the GP would look after them for intermediate visits, but all the blood samples taken at the Welsh practices are sent to the Wrexham Maelor. Therefore, when a patient comes to me at the Countess for review I am at a loss because I am unable to access those results. [...] If I am unable to get those results, I have an incomplete consultation.[53]

The Royal College of Physicians told us that many of their members repeated tests as this was often faster than waiting for the original results to be made available, leading to a "wasteful duplication".[54]

66. The Welsh NHS Confederation also explained that the lack of IT compatibility had an impact on continuity of care, once patients were discharged from hospital:

---

53   Q165
54   Royal College of Physicians (CBH0021)

While hospitals in England can pass discharge information electronically to GP practices managed by English primary care organisations, they cannot do so to Welsh practices. GPs in Wales do not get patients' results or reports electronically from English hospitals therefore causing delay in accessing information in a timely manner. The delay in information sharing could potentially put Welsh patients, post-discharge, at a higher risk than English patients from the same hospital. [...] The reverse may also be true if an English patient receives treatment in a Welsh hospital which can otherwise access and transfer information back out electronically.[55]

67. There is currently no joint programme of work between NHS England and the Welsh Government around central IT arrangements,[56] despite the Department of Health and the Welsh Government agreeing that patient safety and care require effective integration of IT systems.[57] However, we do note that the two Governments are looking to achieve this in different ways. The Department of Health told us that it was focused on developing standards to improve the inter-operability for local IT systems in England, "rather than putting all of one's eggs in one basket and thereby relying on a single national IT system".[58] In contrast, the Welsh Government told us that it was looking to develop a "single national system" that would allow patient information to follow the patient.[59]

68. The Welsh Government told us that it was currently working on establishing electronic referrals between Welsh GPs and English hospitals "so that everything is more automated and speedier for patients".[60] A number of pilots had taken place between GPs in Powys and English hospitals and these would be extended to additional practices in Powys.

69. **It is essential that patient information is transferred between primary and secondary and tertiary services as well as across borders in a timely and consistent manner. It is clear that the existence of different IT systems in England and Wales is having a detrimental impact on patient care in both countries. While we welcome the efforts being made to introduce consistent systems within each country, there must be a commitment to work towards a solution to accommodate the flow of patients across the Wales-England border. We welcome the pilot project currently being run by the Welsh Government in Powys.**

70. *We recommend that the UK Government and the Welsh Government work together to examine how improvements can be made in the electronic transfer of information between Wales and England.*

---

55   Welsh NHS Confederation (CBH0016)

56   Q287

57   Welsh Government oral evidence (CBH0051), Q289

58   Q288

59   Q356

60   Ibid

GP Performers Lists

71. All GPs who perform primary medical services must appear on a Performers List. The list provides an extra layer of reassurance for the public that GPs practising in the NHS are suitably qualified, have up to date training and have passed all relevant checks. Currently each constituent part of the United Kingdom has different Performers Lists.

72. Witnesses told us that separate Performers Lists in England and Wales had a detrimental impact on recruitment to GP practices in Wales and "affected work force movement both ways across the border".[61] The Welsh NHS Confederation told us that many GPs chose not to go through the process of applying separately for inclusion on the Welsh list.[62] The British Medical Association (BMA) explained that GPs on the English Performers List were unable to take up immediately vacancies that existed in practices in Wales.[63]

73. The BMA also said that separate lists had an impact on the availability of locums for border practices, as locums on the English Performers Lists were unable to undertake work in Welsh practices and vice versa. This therefore impacted the choice of locums available to border practices.[64]

74. When we raised the issue with the Health Minister in the Welsh Government, he acknowledged that it was not acceptable that a separate Performers List could prevent people from working either side of the border. He told us that he would move to amend the necessary regulation in Wales[65] to remove barriers to GPs providing services on either side of the border.[66]

75. **Wales is currently facing recruitment challenges in relation to GPs. It is unacceptable that the need for separate Performers Lists is acting as a deterrent to GP recruitment and affecting the freedom of GPs to work cross-border. We welcome the Welsh Government Minister's recognition of this problem during our evidence session, and his commitment to finding a solution.**

76. *We recommend that the Department of Health works with its counterparts in the devolved administrations to establish a single Performers List for GPs across the UK.*

---

61   Q157

62   Q29

63   British Medical Association (CBH0042)

64   Ibid

65   The National Health Service (Performers Lists) (Wales) Regulation 2004

66   Q339

5   Waiting times

77. As we noted earlier, one of the areas in which health policy in England and Wales has diverged is in the targets set for waiting times. In England, the maximum waiting time target is 18 weeks from referral to start of treatment. In Wales, there is a longer maximum waiting time target of 26 weeks from referral to start of treatment.

78. In addition, different arrangements apply to the treatment of patients from across the border in England and Wales. Welsh providers are required to work to the standards and targets set out by the Welsh Government for all patients whom they see and treat, whether they are patients registered in Wales or patients treated in Wales from any other part of the UK. English providers are required to work to the standards and targets set out by the Department of Health for patients who are the responsibility of English commissioners. Services accessed in England by patients registered in Wales are commissioned by Welsh commissioners to meet Welsh Government performance targets.

Dealing with different targets

79. Witnesses told us that the existence of different waiting time targets in the Welsh and English NHS caused significant problems for clinicians, administrators and ultimately patients.[67]

80. The BMA told us that longer waiting times caused problems to Welsh GPs and their workload:

> We are having to see those patients more regularly; we are writing expedite letters on a daily basis, which takes up GP and secretarial time. From time to time, patients ask 'Were I an English resident registered with an English GP, would the wait be different?[68]

81. A number of English providers referred to the additional administrative burden of differentiating between waiting times as an area of difficulty. Shropshire Clinical Commissioning Group highlighted the difficulties of treating Welsh patients in line with Welsh targets:

> In reality this means [...] English hospitals on the border are running with two sets of targets English and Welsh. This can lead to communication issues with patients as some consultants have said directly to them that Welsh patients aren't managed to the same targets because they as a provider are not paid to do so.[69]

---

67   Welsh NHS Confederation (CBH0016)

68   Q178

69   Shropshire Clinical Commissioning Group (CBH0011)

82. Anecdotal evidence we received from patients showed that it was possible for a Welsh patient to wait longer for treatment at an English hospital than an English patient with a similar complaint, due to the difference in waiting time targets between the two administrations.[70] The BMA stated that this did not "sit easily" with clinicians.[71]

83. It is important to note that this difference only affects elective treatment. There was no suggestion that Wales-registered patients would ever wait longer than English-registered patients for clinically urgent treatments. However, the Committee received representation that the differential in waiting times was unfair. Powys Teaching Health Board commented that patients saw waiting times as a 'two-tier service' where there was a level of guarantee that treatment would be sooner for English patients treated in England.[72]

84. Patients argued that they were paying the same taxes, irrespective of which side of the border they lived, and should therefore be treated equally. The BMA called for waiting time standards to be the same on both sides of the border:

> We treat people in the same way, so it would be helpful to us to have things the same. To have two different standards when you are doing one thing is not that helpful ...[73]

85. Jane Ellison told us that hospitals in England were acting to targets set by the Welsh Government, and that they were not treating Welsh-registered patients as second-class citizens:

> No one is saying "The Welshman can wait a bit longer" [...] The Welsh have set a 26-week waiting time standard. The Welsh Government can decide to set a different waiting time standard. In England, we have set it [...] at 18 weeks. That is a decision for the Welsh Government.[74]

86. **Many Clinical Commissioning Groups operate two waiting lists, which differentiate between patients on whether they are 'Welsh' patients or 'English' patients. It is our view that providers should not be in this position; the procedures that English hospitals need to operate in this situation are a matter for the Welsh Government and the Department of Health to resolve.**

---

70   Q137

71   Q193

72   Powys Teaching Health Board (CBH0026)

73   Q194

74   Q278

6   Cross-border engagement and co-ordination

Cross-border patient engagement

87. It is generally accepted that patients and the public need to be enabled to play a greater role in the care they receive and to engage effectively in health policy development. In this section, we examine public awareness of the difference in services they can expect to receive in England and Wales, and public engagement in matters affecting health policy.

Raising awareness

88. There is a lack of awareness and understanding among patients and service users about devolution and healthcare. A poll conducted by the BBC highlighted that less than half of the population in Wales were aware that the NHS was the responsibility of the Welsh Government.[75] The poll showed that 48% of the population knew Welsh Ministers had responsibility for health while 43% thought it was the UK Government.

89. During our public events in Newtown and Hereford, we heard that many patients on both sides of the border were generally unaware of the potential for divergence between the Welsh and English health services. The Welsh NHS Confederation said that patients were not aware that choosing a GP on one side of the border might affect later referrals:

> … it is quite possible to have two people living next door to each other in either Wales or England registered as patients with two different practices and subject to two different health policies.[76]

90. The Royal College of Physicians told us that a lack of awareness about the different health systems meant that clinicians often had to have "difficult" conversations with patients, explaining why there was access to different treatment or drugs in each respective nation.[77]

91. Witnesses from both sides of the border called for improved communication with cross-border patients, which needed "to be standardised and consistent across the Department of Health and the Welsh Government".[78]

92. The Department of Health told us that information regarding the different health systems was available on NHS England's website,[79] while the BMA told us that they had had discussions with the Welsh Government about a website for Welsh patients.[80]

---

75   www.bbc.co.uk/news/uk-wales-politics-27739205

76   Welsh NHS Confederation (CBH0016)

77   Royal College of Physicians (CBH0021)

78   Q6

79   Q293

80   Q192

However, some witnesses had concerns about relying on the internet to disseminate information, as many people living in the cross-border areas had limited or no access at all to the internet.[81] Shropshire Clinical Commissioning Group told us that they encouraged their GPs to explain the differences to their patients before they were referred to secondary care "so that the patient is making an informed decision" about the impact of GP registration.[82]

93. **Some patients living on the border area of England and Wales choose their GP based on proximity. We are concerned that patients are unaware of the differences in services they can expect to receive in England and Wales. Better information for patients must be made available, particularly in immediate border areas, where the choice of a Welsh or English GP might have implications for later care.**

94. *We recommend that the Department of Health and the Welsh Government work together with medical practitioners, particularly at a GP level, to ensure that patients are better informed of the differences in healthcare policy between England and Wales. Patients must also be made aware of the impact of choosing a Welsh or English GP and the implications that this might have for later care.*

Patient engagement

95. Healthcare policy on one side of the border can have an impact on patients on the other. During our inquiry, we received evidence that patients accessing health care services on a cross-border basis felt that they were unable to contribute to the development of the services which they and their families use.

96. As we have discussed, many patients in Wales have no choice but to receive secondary care in England. For example, Powys has no district general hospital and is served by the Royal Shrewsbury Hospital and Princess Royal Hospital in Telford, among others. The future of Shrewsbury's accident and emergency department is currently being debated as part of the Future Fit programme.[83]

97. During our public events, Welsh patients expressed concern that they could be adversely affected if services were moved eastwards, with them having to travel further to receive care. Witnesses expressed concern that the changes could occur without input from them, and without realisation of the impact it could have for Welsh patients.

98. When we put these concerns to Shropshire Clinical Commissioning Group, it told us that it had held a number of engagement exercises with the population in Powys, including

---

81   Shropshire Council (CBH0050)

82   Q101

83   The Future Fit Programme has been set up to develop a clear vision for hospital services to serve the population of Shropshire, Telford & Wrekin and mid Wales.

a number of public meetings, a telephone survey, and a number of workshops in August and September.[84]

99. English residents who receive GP and hospital care in Wales also expressed concern about their ability to affect services in Wales. Healthwatch was established in England in April 2013 and is the new consumer champion for health and social care. It aims to "give citizens and communities a stronger voice to influence and challenge how health and social care services are provided within their locality".[85] However, Action4OurCare told us that it had no remit in Wales, while Welsh Community Health Councils could only represent Welsh residents, and not those receiving treatment in Wales.[86]

100. Both Governments agreed on the importance of cross-border patient engagement and representation.[87] NHS England agreed that it was a "crucial principle" that patient's interests were considered when designing and delivering services, irrespective of whether someone was a Welsh or English resident.[88] The Welsh Health Minister also noted that, while his primary responsibility was to Welsh residents, he felt a responsibility to English residents who accessed services in Wales.[89]

101. **We welcome the commitment that exists to engage the public in service delivery. However, we note that patients still feel disenfranchised from any decision taken on those services, particularly when they are provided across the border. The decision-making processes on each side of the border need to be more co-ordinated, more coherent and transparent.**

102. *We recommend that NHS Wales and NHS England work together to improve patient engagement for cross-border services.*

Engagement between Local Health Board and CCGs

103. As well as care to individual patients, large-scale service delivery by LHBs or CCGs can be affected by cross-border activity. Health representatives told us that relationships between LHBs and CCGs on the border were positive. Shropshire CCG told us that Powys Health Board had a place on its programme board and had a vote, as did Shropshire CCG and the Telford and Wrekin CCG: "so its vote on that programme board is proportionate".[90] However, we heard concerns that changes to areas such as community services and to community hospitals were not being communicated to neighbouring healthcare providers across the border.

---

84   Q114

85   www.nhs.uk/NHSEngland/thenhs/about/Pages/getinvolved.aspx

86   Action4OurCare (CBH005)

87   Q39

88   Q290

89   Q381

90   Q118

104. Shropshire CCG told us that changes to minor injuries provision in Chirk had meant an increase in the number of patients arriving at Oswestry. It told us that, "when [decisions] have implications across the border for capacity and for the planning of health services, it would be helpful to know of them in advance".[91]

105. The Welsh Government expressed concern that English local authorities were sending Looked After Children (LAC), some of whom have specialist or mental health needs, for placement in Wales, without appropriate discussion and notification with LHBs. The Welsh Government's Health Minister told us that this had resource implications for LHBs, particularly in rural areas where "services are not equipped to respond to very significant and unexpected needs".[92] Although we do not examine this issue further in this inquiry, the financial implications of such services being provided cross-border may require further investigation in the next Parliament.

106. The Welsh NHS Confederation told us that it would welcome formal protocols to be put in place to ensure formal consultation between LHBs and CCGs when services impact on populations across the border.[93]

107. **We are encouraged by the positive evidence we have heard regarding hospitals which have included a cross-border dimension in their management structures. We believe that this model could and should be replicated in all hospitals near the border which serve both English and Welsh patients.**

108. **We are concerned that there is a lack of communication regarding changes to healthcare services which could have an impact across the border.** *We recommend that formal protocols are put in place to ensure consultation between LHBs and CCGs when changes to services impact on populations across the border.*

---

91   Q116

92   Q351

93   Q39

Conclusions and recommendations

Funding and Commissioning

1. There is an unresolved tension between the cross-border healthcare protocol and the Health and Social Care Act 2012. English patients registered with Welsh GPs or Welsh-registered GPs do not receive the same services as if they were registered with an English GP, and for the majority of people concerned, they will not have a choice of registering with an English GP. (Paragraph 30)

2. The Department of Health should investigate the problem of why some patients living in England, currently being treated in the Welsh healthcare system and wishing to be treated in the English healthcare system, have been turned away by GP practices in England. This should be considered in light of the legal rights of these residents under the Health and Social Care Act 2012. (Paragraph 31)

3. We recommend that the Welsh and UK Governments continue to work together to clarify what an English patient registered with a Welsh GP and a Welsh-registered GP, and a Welsh patient registered with an English GP and an English-registered GP, can expect. (Paragraph 32)

4. We welcome the good relationship between Local Health Boards in Wales and the Clinical Commissioning Groups in England. The publication of the financial accounts of such bodies will enable the public to see whether value for money is being achieved. (Paragraph 42)

Cross-border problems

5. Cross-border movements have been a fact of life for many years, and this is no less the case for health services. For those residing in immediate border areas, the nearest health provider may not be in their country of residence. There is no practical or realistic prospect of diverting these well-established cross-border flows, nor would it be desirable to do so. (Paragraph 51)

6. We welcome the commitment from the Welsh Government's Health Minister on patient needs and his commitment not to allow the border to become a barrier. We recognise that Welsh GPs will be mindful of a need to maintain investment and capacity in Wales. Healthcare providers in England and Wales need to maintain close links to ensure that patients receive the treatment they need regardless of their country of residence, particularly given the policy divergence that has emerged as a result of devolution. (Paragraph 52)

7. Specialised services are accessed by patients from all across Wales. It is unacceptable that administrative issues lead to delays to patients seeking specialised services. (Paragraph 61)

8.   We recommend that Welsh Local Health Boards must provide improved training for clinicians on how to refer patients for tertiary care. (Paragraph 61)

9.   The divergence in policy since devolution can cause difficulties in cross-border contracts. There must be improvements to service level agreements (SLAs) between LHBs and CCGs. (Paragraph 62)

10. We recommend that the Department of Health and the Welsh Government work together to carry out a review of cross-border SLAs. (Paragraph 62)

11. Uncertainty in the referral process can cause unnecessary worry to patients and their families, particularly when they are their most vulnerable. Decisions must be made in a timely manner. (Paragraph 63)

12. We recommend that a 30-day limit be placed on decisions on referrals by WHSSC (Paragraph 63)

13. It is essential that patient information is transferred between primary and secondary and tertiary services as well as across borders in a timely and consistent manner. It is clear that the existence of different IT systems in England and Wales is having a detrimental impact on patient care in both countries. While we welcome the efforts being made to introduce consistent systems within each country, there must be a commitment to work towards a solution to accommodate the flow of patients across the Wales-England border. We welcome the pilot project currently being run by the Welsh Government in Powys. (Paragraph 69)

14. We recommend that the UK Government and the Welsh Government work together to examine how improvements can be made in the electronic transfer of information between Wales and England. (Paragraph 70)

15. Wales is currently facing recruitment challenges in relation to GPs. It is unacceptable that the need for separate Performers Lists is acting as a deterrent to GP recruitment and affecting the freedom of GPs to work cross-border. We welcome the Welsh Government Minister's recognition of this problem during our evidence session, and his commitment to finding a solution. (Paragraph 75)

16. We recommend that the Department of Health works with its counterparts in the devolved administrations to establish a single Performers List for GPs across the UK. (Paragraph 76)

Waiting times

17. Many Clinical Commissioning Groups operate two waiting lists, which differentiate between patients on whether they are 'Welsh' patients or 'English' patients. It is our view that providers should not be in this position; the procedures that English hospitals need to operate in this situation are a matter for the Welsh Government and the Department of Health to resolve. (Paragraph 86)

Cross-border engagement and co-ordination

18. Some patients living on the border area of England and Wales choose their GP based on proximity. We are concerned that patients are unaware of the differences in services they can expect to receive in England and Wales. Better information for patients must be made available, particularly in immediate border areas, where the choice of a Welsh or English GP might have implications for later care. (Paragraph 93)

19. We recommend that the Department of Health and the Welsh Government work together with medical practitioners, particularly at a GP level, to ensure that patients are better informed of the differences in healthcare policy between England and Wales. Patients must also be made aware of the impact of choosing a Welsh or English GP and the implications that this might have for later care. (Paragraph 94)

20. We welcome the commitment that exists to engage the public in service delivery. However, we note that patients still feel disenfranchised from any decision taken on those services, particularly when they are provided across the border. The decision-making processes on each side of the border need to be more co-ordinated, more coherent and transparent. (Paragraph 101)

21. We recommend that NHS Wales and NHS England work together to improve patient engagement for cross-border services. (Paragraph 102)

22. We are encouraged by the positive evidence we have heard regarding hospitals which have included a cross-border dimension in their management structures. We believe that this model could and should be replicated in all hospitals near the border which serve both English and Welsh patients. (Paragraph 107)

23. We are concerned that there is a lack of communication regarding changes to healthcare services which could have an impact across the border. (Paragraph 108)

24. We recommend that formal protocols are put in place to ensure consultation between LHBs and CCGs when changes to services impact on populations across the border. (Paragraph 108)

Annex: Summary of public events in Newtown and Hereford

Key themes from Newtown meeting

- **Lack of clarity:** The cross-border protocol, boundaries, and even the fact that health had been devolved was not clear to patients. The confusion about where patients could go, what treatments they could receive, and to whom they could complain to caused frustration for patients and even delays in treatment, as not even practitioners fully understood it.

- **Unfairness:** Some Welsh patients felt like they were treated as second-class citizens by the English NHS. Attendees said that they were pushed down waiting lists by English hospitals and could not get referrals to specialists. They also felt that it was unfair that some cancer drugs could be obtained on one side of the border but not the other.

- **Unhappiness with funding for Powys:** Attendees felt that Powys was neglected by the Welsh Government and did not receive enough healthcare funding. They felt this was exacerbated by its position on the border, as they had to rely on English hospitals that did not take their needs into account.

- **Lack of consultation:** English hospitals and CCGs were not doing enough to consult Welsh patients on changes to their services, despite relying on Welsh patients for funding. Attendees felt that they were being ignored and that services that they relied on were being moved out of reach.

- **Wider issues for healthcare in Powys:** Cross-border issues are part of the larger challenges of providing a large rural area like Powys with healthcare, including the lack of transport, ambulance times, the difficulty of making hospitals and services viable, and the recruitment of key staff.

- **GPs and key staff:** It was difficult to recruit GPs, nurses, and specialists to rural areas like Powys and difficult to retain them. At the same time, more GPs were going part time, reducing the levels of care available to residents.

- **Lack of communication:** Attendees identified poor communication and co-operation between health services on either side of the border as a major barrier to patients receiving care. In particular, records and notes were often lost or not transferred between hospitals in time.

- **Welsh language:** There were issues for people for whom Welsh was their first language being understood in English hospitals, particularly to healthcare workers recruited from abroad on the basis of their proficiency in English.

Summary: Attendees wanted a *National* [their emphasis] Health Service and to be treated fairly and equally to English people.

Key themes from Hereford meeting

- **English GPs for English residents**: There were not enough English GPs for attendees to register with. This meant that some patients were forced to register with Welsh GPs, removing them from the English NHS. For many patients, this was a key issue that they felt strongly about.

- **Loss of rights and the principle of choice**: English attendees frequently said that they felt that they were being denied access to the English NHS and were being deprived of their rights under the NHS constitution. In particular, they emphasised that they did not have any choice when it came to GPs and are being forced into the Welsh NHS. Attendees believed that access to the English NHS should be guaranteed by English residency.

- **More cooperation and clearer agreements needed**: There had been disputes over payments between Powys and the trusts it contracts. Information was not shared as well as it could be. There was a need to integrate care better in order for cross-border health to work. Attendees suggested that the protocol might need to be re-written and contracts and agreements made clearer in order for cross-border healthcare to work.

- **Poor communication within NHS**: Welsh health boards were failing to communicate with their English counterparts, making co-operation and effective cross-border care difficult. In particular, unclear agreements between health boards and English hospitals made it difficult for English hospitals to plan and budget for Welsh patients. Incompatible IT systems and the difficulties of transferring records and notes also make it difficult for patients to cross the border and receive treatment.

- **Poor communication with patients**: Attendees felt that they had not been kept adequately informed of policy changes and were not informed of the consequences of devolution or of registering with a Welsh GP. The absence of information meant that they were often unable to make an informed choice: this had led to a loss of trust in the NHS.

- **Unnecessary barriers**: The devolution of health had led to unnecessary duplication and difference in standards, making integrated care and referrals more difficult. This included additional registration requirements for GPs, waiting lists, and available treatments and drugs.

Summary: English residents should be able to use the English NHS and should have choice. Failing that, cross-border co-operation and information sharing must be improved.

Formal Minutes

Tuesday 10 March 2015

Members present:

David T.C. Davies, in the Chair

Geraint Davies	Simon Hart
Glyn Davies	Mrs Siân C. James
Jonathan Edwards	Jessica Morden
Nia Griffith	Mr Mark Williams

Draft Report (*Cross-border health arrangements between England and Wales*), proposed by the Chair, brought up and read.

Ordered, That the draft Report be read a second time, paragraph by paragraph.

Paragraphs 1 to 108 read and agreed to.

Annex and Summary agreed to.

Resolved, That the Report be the Third Report of the Committee to the House.

Ordered, That the Chair make the Report to the House.

Ordered, That embargoed copies of the Report be made available (Standing Order No. 134).

The following written evidence was ordered to be reported to the House for publication and to be placed in the Library and Parliamentary Archives:

1   Ms K Allen, Herefordshire
2   Mrs H Phillips, Chepstow
3   Mr I Smith, Abergavenny
4   Ms L Hole, Monmouth

[Adjourned till Tuesday 17 March at 2.15 pm.

Witnesses

The following witnesses gave evidence. Transcripts can be viewed on the Committee's inquiry page at www.parliament.uk/welshcom.

Tuesday 18 November 2014   *Question number*

Alan Brace, Interim Deputy Chief Executive and Director of Finance and Procurement, Aneurin Bevan University Health Board, **Angela Hopkins**, Executive Director of Nursing and Midwifery, Betsi Cadwaladr University Health Board, and **Helen Birtwhistle**, Director, Welsh NHS Confederation   Q1-41

Jesse Norman, MP for Hereford and South Herefordshire, and **Pamela Plummer**, Action4OurCare   Q42-81

Tuesday 2 December 2014

Tony Chambers, Chief Executive, Countess of Chester Hospital, **Caroline Smith**, Senior Quality Manager, Engagement and Inclusion, Gloucestershire Clinical Commissioning Group, and **Dr Julie Davies**, Director of Strategy and Service Redesign, Shropshire Clinical Commissioning Group   Q82-133

Councillor Darren Mayor, Portfolio Holder for Adult Social Services, Powys County Council, and **Frederick Geoffrey Davies**, Vice-Chair of the Visiting, Monitoring and Scrutiny Committee, Brecknock and Radnor Community Health Council   Q134-148

Tuesday 16 December 2014

Dr Alan Rees RCP, Vice President for Wales, Royal College of Physicians, **Dr Frank Joseph RCP**, Acute Care Fellow, Royal College of Physicians, **Dr Stephen Kelly**, Welsh Consultants Committee, British Medical Association Wales, and **Dr Peter Horvarth-Howard**, General Practitioners Committee, British Medical Association Wales   Q149-235

Jane Ellison MP, Parliamentary Under-Secretary of State, Department of Health, **Ben Dyson**, Director of NHS Group, Department of Health, and **Ian Dodge**, National Director for Commissioning Strategy, NHS England   Q236-296

Thursday 8 January 2015

John Hill-Tout, Interim Chair, Welsh Health Specialised Services Committee, **Stuart Davies**, Director of Finance, Welsh Health Specialised Services Committee, and **John Palmer**, Director of Specialised and Tertiary Services, Welsh Health Specialised Services Committee   Q297-330

Mark Drakeford AM, Minister for Health and Social Services, Welsh Government, and **Dr Andrew Goodall**, Chief Executive, NHS Wales   Q331-381

Published written evidence

The following written evidence was received and can be viewed on the Committee's inquiry web page at www.parliament.uk/welshcom. INQ numbers are generated by the evidence processing system and so may not be complete.

1   2Gether NHSF Trust (CBH0041)

2   Action4OurCare (CBH0005)

3   Betsi Cadwaladr University Health Board (CBH0019)

4   Bishop's Castle Patients Group (CBH0043)

5   Brecknock And Radnor Community Health Council And Montgomeryshire Community Health Council (CBH0004)

6   British Medical Association (CBH0042)

7   Cheshire West And Chester Council (CBH0008)

8   Comisiynydd Y Gymraeg / Welsh Language Commissioner (CBH0031)

9   Department of Health (CBH0030)

10   Department of Health (CBH0049)

11   Department of Health (CBH0055)

12   Genetic Alliance UK (CBH0020)

13   Healthwatch Shropshire (CBH0003)

14   Jane Dodds, Montgomeryshire (CBH0014)

15   Jesse Norman MP for Hereford and South Herefordshire (CBH0018)

16   Major (Retired) R. Taylor, Gloucestershire (CBH0009)

17   Mr C H Wynn-Jones FRCS, Welshpool (CBH0039)

18   Mr K. W. Ivin, Tutshill (CBH0034)

19   Mrs A Mulholland, Cardiff (CBH0053)

20   Ms D. Mariana Robinson, Monmouth (CBH0033)

21   Ms E. Swinglehurst, Herefordshire (CBH0001)

22   Ms J. Thompson, Monmouth (CBH0006)

23   Ms S. Hunt, Monmouth (CBH0010)

24   Ms S. Stevens, Flintshire (CBH0045)

25   Ms V. Medley, Monmouth (CBH0028)

26   Neuro Voice Powys (CBH0012)

27   NHS Gloucestershire Clinical Commissioning Group (CBH0035)

28   NHS West Cheshire Clinical Commissioning Group (CBH0017)

29   Older People's Commissioner For Wales (CBH0002)

30   Powys County Council (CBH0032)

31   Powys Teaching Health Board (CBH0026)

32   Rarer Cancers Foundation (CBH0022)

33   Rarer Cancers Foundation (CBH0054)

34   Royal College Of Physicians (CBH0021)

35   Royal Pharmaceutical Society (CBH0048)

36   Shropshire Clinical Commissioning Group (CBH0011)

37   Shropshire Clinical Commissioning Group (CBH0052)

38   Shropshire Council (CBH0024)

39   Shropshire Council (CBH0050)

40   St Briavels Parish Council (CBH0023)

41   Tenovus (CBH0015)

42   Royal College of Surgeons of Edinburgh (CBH0047)

43   Welsh NHS Confederation (CBH0016)

44   Welsh Government (CBH0051)

45   Welsh Health Specialised Services Committee (CBH0040)

Unpublished evidence

The following written evidence has been reported to the House, but has not been published. Copies have been placed in the House of Commons Library, where they may be inspected by Members. Other copies are in the Parliamentary Archives, and are available to the public for inspection. Requests to inspect them should be addressed to The Parliamentary Archives, Houses of Parliament, London SW1A 0PW (tel. 020 7219 3074). Opening hours are from 9.30 am to 5.00 pm on Mondays to Fridays.

Ms K Allen, Herefordshire

Mrs H Phillips, Chepstow

Mr I Smith, Abergavenny

Ms L Hole, Monmouth

List of Reports from the Committee during the current Parliament

All publications from the Committee are available on the Committee's website at www.parliament.uk/welshcom.

The reference number of the Government's response to each Report is printed in brackets after the HC printing number.

Session 2014–15

First Report	Energy generation in Wales: Shale Gas	HC 284
Second Report	International representation and promotion of Wales by UK bodies	HC 337
First Special Report	Energy generation in Wales: Shale Gas: Government Response to the Committees First Report of Session 2014–15	HC 662
Second Special Report	International representation and promotion of Wales by UK bodies: Government Response to the Committee's Second Report of Session 2014–15	HC 927

Session 2013–14

First Report	The Voluntary Code of Practice in the dairy sector	HC 155
Second Report	The impact of changes to housing benefit in Wales	HC 159
Third Report	The Work Programme in Wales	HC 264
First Special Report	Crossing the border—road and rail links between England and Wales: Government Response to the Committee's Third Report of Session 2012–13	HC 158
Second Special Report	Support for Armed Forces Veterans in Wales: Government Response to the Committee's Second Report of Session 2012–13	HC 263
Third Special Report	The Voluntary Code of Practice in the dairy sector: Government Response to the Committee's First Report of Session 2013–14	HC 635
Fourth Special Report	The impact of changes to housing benefit in Wales: Government Response to the Committee's Second Report of Session 2013–14	HC 1012
Fifth Special Report	The Work Programme in Wales: Government Response to the Committee's Third Report of Session 2013–14	HC 1035
Fourth Report	Pre-legislative scrutiny of the draft Wales Bill	HC 962
Sixth Special Report	Pre-legislative scrutiny of the draft Wales Bill: Government Response to the Committee's Fourth Report of Session 2013–14	HC 1205

Session 2012–2013

First Report	Broadband Services in Wales	HC 580
Second Report	Support for Armed Forces Veterans in Wales	HC 131
Third Report	Crossing the border: road and rail links between England and Wales	HC 95
First Special Report	Representation of consumer interests in Wales: Government Response to the Committee's Seventh Report of Session 2010–12	HC 111
Second Special Report	Inward Investment in Wales: Government Response to the Committee's Eighth Report of Session 2010–12	HC 125
Third Special Report	Broadband Services in Wales: Ofcom Response to the Committee's First Report of Session 2012–13	HC 806

Session 2010–12

First Special Report	Welsh prisoners in the prison estate: follow up: Government Response to the Committee's Ninth Report of Session 2009-10	HC 398
Second Special Report	Wales and Whitehall: Government Response to the Committee's Eleventh Report of Session 2009-10	HC 399
Third Special Report	Cross-border provision of public services for Wales: follow up: Government Response to the Committee's Tenth Report of Session 2009-10	HC 419
First Report	The implications for Wales of the Government's proposals on constitutional reform	HC 495
Second Report	The proposed amendment of Schedule 7 to the Government of Wales Act 2006	HC 603
Third Report	The Severn Crossings Toll	HC 506
Fourth Special Report	The implications for Wales of the Government's proposals on constitutional reform - Government's Response to the Committee's First Report of Session 2010-11	HC 729
Fourth Report	The future of the Newport Passport Office	HC 590
Fifth Special Report	The Severn Crossings Toll: Government Response to the Committee's Third Report of Session 2010-11	HC 837
Sixth Special Report	Proposed Legislative Competence Orders relating to Organ Donation and Cycle Paths	HC 896-I
Seventh Special Report	The proposed amendment of Schedule 7 to the Government of Wales Act 2006: Government Response to the Committee's Second Report of Session 2010-11	HC 918
Fifth Report	S4C	HC 614
Sixth Report	Pre-appointment hearing with the Government's preferred candidate for the Chairman of the S4C Authority	HC 1061-I
Seventh Report	Representation of consumer interests in Wales	HC 1558-I

Eighth Report   Inward Investment in Wales   HC 854-I

ISBN 978-0-215-08409-5

PEFC
PEFC/16-33-622   Printed in the United Kingdom by The Stationery Office Limited
                             3/2015   48287   19585